Chatterbox

ENGLISH AS A SECOND LANGUAGE

Gillian Baxter
Jonathan Munro Jones
Hélène Bibeau

THIRD CYCLE, ELEMENTARY

ACTIVITY BOOK 2

ANSWER KEY

ÉDITIONS DU RENOUVEAU PÉDAGOGIQUE INC.

5757, RUE CYPIHOT
SAINT-LAURENT (QUÉBEC)
H4S 1R3

TÉLÉPHONE : (514) 334-2690
TÉLÉCOPIEUR : (514) 334-4720
COURRIEL : erpidlm@erpi.com

Project editor
Jocelyne Lauzière

Cover and book design
Tandem Conception et Infographie inc.

Illustrations
Danielle Bélanger: pages 1-8, 12-18, 31-48, 58-70, 77-90, 98-114, 118-128
Jocelyne Bouchard: pages 19-30, 71-76
Irina Georgeta Pusztai: pages 49-57, 91-97
Danièla Zékina: pages 9, 11, 115

© 2003 ÉDITIONS DU RENOUVEAU PÉDAGOGIQUE INC.
Tous droits réservés

Dépôt légal : 2ᵉ trimestre 2003
Bibliothèque nationale du Québec
National Library of Canada
Imprimé au Canada

ISBN 2-7613-1362-3
1234567890 HLN 09876543
10547 ABCD   0F10

Contents

Message to the Teacher

This full-colour Activity Book accompanies Student's Book 2 of the Chatterbox series for the third cycle. It replaces most of the reproducible handouts provided in the Teacher's Guide, thus relieving teachers of the time-consuming task of making photocopies. All instructions are written in clear, simple language, and the number of pictograms has been kept to a minimum to avoid confusion.

Activity Book 2 provides material to accompany the warm-up, the activities and the wrap-up of each unit of Student's Book 2. The Activity Book also contains one or more extension activities in each unit that can be used for remediation or enrichment, in class or at home. In addition, each unit ends with one and sometimes two extra activities that can be used for a variety of purposes.

Pictograms

 This indicates the corresponding page in the Student's Book.

 This section contains a questionnaire for student self-evaluation.

We hope you enjoy using *Chatterbox* and wish you a successful school year.

Chers parents,

Le but du cours d'anglais au primaire est de permettre aux enfants d'acquérir une connaissance fonctionnelle de la langue seconde. Ainsi, dès le premier jour de classe, votre enfant commencera à acquérir le vocabulaire de base et les stratégies d'apprentissage qui lui permettront d'échanger avec ses camarades de classe en anglais. Durant l'année scolaire, votre enfant sera appelé à participer à diverses activités qui visent surtout à développer la communication orale.

Le présent cahier soutient et renforce les activités du manuel de l'élève; il propose également des activités d'enrichissement en lien avec les thèmes abordés en classe. À la fin de chaque activité, de même qu'à la fin de chaque unité, votre enfant aura l'occasion de faire le point sur ses apprentissages à l'aide d'un questionnaire d'auto-évaluation. Nous vous encourageons à consulter régulièrement ces pistes d'évaluation afin de suivre le cheminement de votre enfant.

L'enseignante ou l'enseignant de votre enfant vous proposera des moyens pour poursuivre et consolider l'apprentissage de l'anglais à la maison. Parmi ces moyens, il y a en un qui nous semble plus important que les autres. Ce moyen, c'est de valoriser les efforts de votre enfant dans la langue seconde. L'importance que votre enfant accordera à l'apprentissage de l'anglais dépendra dans une large mesure de l'importance que vous y accorderez.

Recevez, chers parents, nos meilleures salutations.

Les auteurs de *Chatterbox*,

Gillian Baxter

Jonathan Munro Jones

Hélène Bibeau

All about Me!

Name:

Age:

Group:

Glue your photo here.

Favourite animal:

Favourite book:

Favourite cartoon character:

Favourite colour:

Favourite game:

Favourite meal:

Favourite pastime:

Favourite snack:

Favourite treat:

Favourite TV program:

Favourite Web site:

Unit 1

Learning Tools

Warm-up

▶ Write down the first letter of each hidden word.

| a | k | s | t |

▶ Unscramble the letters to find the mystery word. _____ *task* _____

- I found all the hidden words.   Yes ☐   No ☐
- I found the mystery word with ☐ or without ☐ help.

Activity 1 Nonsense

▶ Decode the message.

babble = _____ *English* _____

blah = _____ *world* _____

blip = _____ *speak* _____

- **I decoded the words.**
  All of them ☐   Most of them ☐   Some of them ☐   None of them ☐
- **This activity was fun.**   Yes ☐   No ☐

  **Talk about a Riddle**

▷ Write down the clues.

▷ Use the clues to solve the riddle.

Our Words				Our Solution
school	food	clothes		
book	water	flower		
sport	television			
family	vehicle			

- I used Chatterbox 3 for help. Yes ☐ No ☐
- I worked quietly. Yes ☐ No ☐

SB 7

▶ Make a list of the words you guessed.

My Guess	Solution
Answers will vary.	

- **I spoke English.**
  Always ☐   Most of the time ☐   Some of the time ☐   Never ☐
- **I guessed _____ words with my team.**

Activity 4 — Tons of Tongue Twisters

SB 8

▶ Make a list of the participants in the Tongue-Twister Tournament.

▶ Circle their ratings.

Tongue Twisters	Participants	Rating*		
She sells seashells by the seashore.	*Students will rate the participants in the tournament.*	1	2	3
		1	2	3
		1	2	3
		1	2	3
A big black bug bit a big black bear.		1	2	3
		1	2	3
		1	2	3
		1	2	3
How much wood would a wood-chuck chuck, if a woodchuck could chuck wood?		1	2	3
		1	2	3
		1	2	3
		1	2	3
Peter Piper picked a pail of pickled peppers.		1	2	3
		1	2	3
		1	2	3
		1	2	3
If two witches were watching two watches, which witch would watch which watch?		1	2	3
		1	2	3
		1	2	3
		1	2	3
Happy Henry has hundreds of hens.		1	2	3
		1	2	3
		1	2	3
		1	2	3

* Ratings: 1 = Great!   2 = O.K.   3 = Try again.

- **I used Chatterbox 7 for help.**   Yes ☐   No ☐
- **This activity was:**
  Very easy ☐   Easy ☐   Difficult ☐   Very difficult ☐

Extension Activity

More Tongue Twisters

► **Practise these tongue twisters.**

Students can practise saying these extra tongue twisters.

The hat she has on her head is heavy.

I scream, you scream,
we all scream for ice cream.

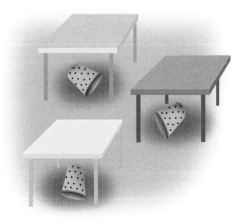

Three tin thimbles are under
three thin tables.

We shall surely see the sun shine soon.

▶ **Glue your tools in the toolbox.**

Students will choose different tools for their toolboxes.

* **I put _____ tools in my toolbox.**
* **I am satisfied with my work.**
  Extremely ☐   Very ☐   Not very ☐   Not at all ☐

What Is It?

► **Guess what the strange words mean.**

1. Paul wrote a **dax** on the board. "That **dax** is wrong," said Amanda.
   "Ten and ten make twenty. Not twelve!"

   A **dax** is:

   a letter   a word   (a number)

2. I **fize** at 12 Oak Street. Where do you **fize**?

   Fize is:

   go   (live)   like

3. My **mox** is brown and white. She likes milk.

   A **mox** is:

   a book   a mother   (a cat)

4. I can't find my **racot**. I put it on my desk. It's my blue one. I need it to do
   my drawing.

   A **racot** is:

   a coat   (a pencil)   a bicycle

5. Everyone liked that book about animals. The teacher **expolsed** it to the
   class.

   Expolsed is:

   (read)   spoke   made

Unit 2

On This Day

Special Events

▶ **Match each event with its picture on page 12 in your book.**

▶ **Write a letter from A to G on the line next to the event.**

Graduation Day _____E_____   Fête nationale _____D_____

Father's Day _____A_____   Helen Keller's birthday _____B_____

World Environment Day _____G_____   The first day of summer _____F_____

Anne Frank's birthday _____C_____

▶ **Write the name of the month on the calendar.**

▶ **Place the events on the calendar.**

June						
Sunday	Monday	Tuesday	Wednesday	Thursday	Friday	Saturday
		1	2	3	4	5 (G) *World Environment Day*
6	7	8	9	10	11	12 (C) *Anne Frank's birthday*
13 (A) *Father's Day*	14	15	16	17	18	19
20	21 (F) *The first day of summer*	22	23	24 (D) *Fête nationale*	25 (E) *Graduation Day*	26
27 (B) *Helen Keller's birthday*	28	29	30			

• **I identified the special events.**

All of them ☐   Most of them ☐   Some of them ☐   None of them ☐

• **I already knew about** _____ .

• **I learned about** _____ .

Extension Activity

June Celebrations

▶ Find out more about one of these special events.

Graduation Day

Father's Day

World Environment Day

Anne Frank's birthday

Fête nationale

Helen Keller's birthday

The first day of summer

I would like to find out more about *Answers will vary.* _____ .

I learned that _____
_____
_____
_____ .

▶ **Listen to the recording.**

▶ **Write the events on the timeline.**

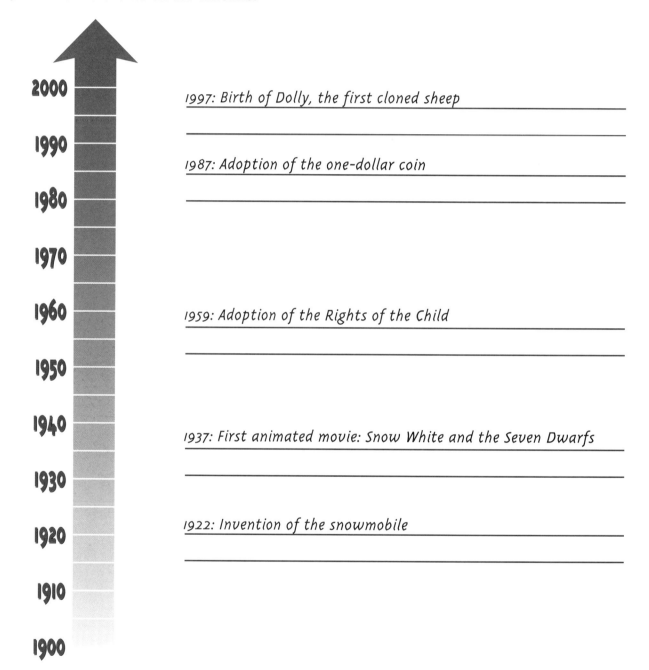

2000

1997: Birth of Dolly, the first cloned sheep

1990

1987: Adoption of the one-dollar coin

1980

1970

1960

1959: Adoption of the Rights of the Child

1950

1940

1937: First animated movie: Snow White and the Seven Dwarfs

1930

1920

1922: Invention of the snowmobile

1910

1900

• **I understood the news reports on the recording.**
All of them ☐   Most of them ☐   Some of them ☐   None of them ☐

• **This activity was:**
Very easy ☐   Easy ☐   Difficult ☐   Very difficult ☐

▶ Read the texts on page 14 in your book.

▶ Write down the headline for each text.

Letter 1

The Habs do it again!

_____

_____

Letter 2

Man walks on the moon

_____

_____

E-mail message

The Ice Age comes to Québec

_____

_____

Postcard

Let the Games begin!

_____

_____

- **I found the key words in each text.**
  All of them ☐   Most of them ☐   Some of them ☐   None of them ☐
- **I learned something new in this activity.**   Yes ☐ No ☐

Activity **3** A Cause for Celebration

▶ Write how you celebrate your birthday.

Students will write how they celebrate their birthdays.

▶ Make a candle for your birthday cake.
▶ Write your name and birthday on the candle.

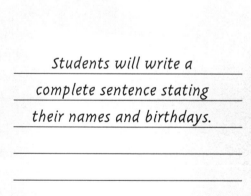

*Students will write a
complete sentence stating
their names and birthdays.*

Continued on next page

Activity 3   **A Cause for Celebration (continued)**

▶ Find out who shares your birthday month.

▶ Write their names on the birthday cake.

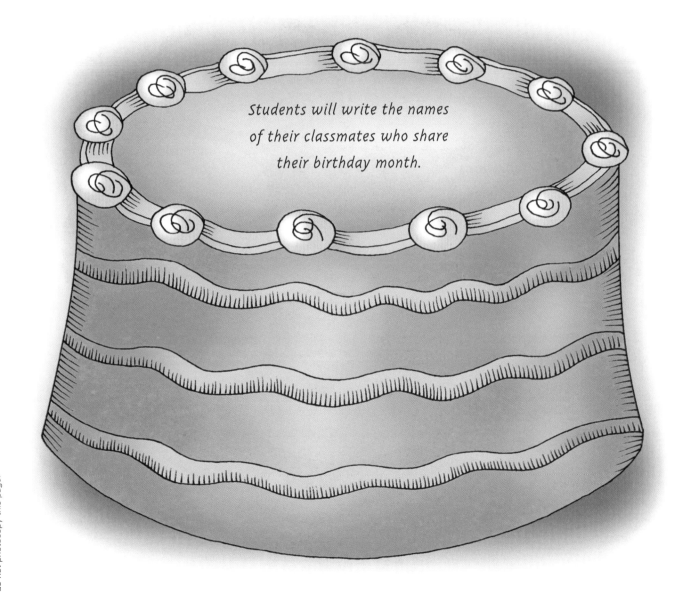

Students will write the names of their classmates who share their birthday month.

- **I discovered which classmates share my birthday month.**   Yes ☐   No ☐
- **I used Chatterbox 3 for help.**   Yes ☐   No ☐
- **I spoke English during this activity.**
  Always ☐   Most of the time ☐   Some of the time ☐   Never ☐

Activity 4 My Day in History

▶ **Find some events that happened on the date you were born.**

▶ **Place them in the appropriate category.**

Students will find out about events that happened on their birthdates. They will place each event in the appropriate category.

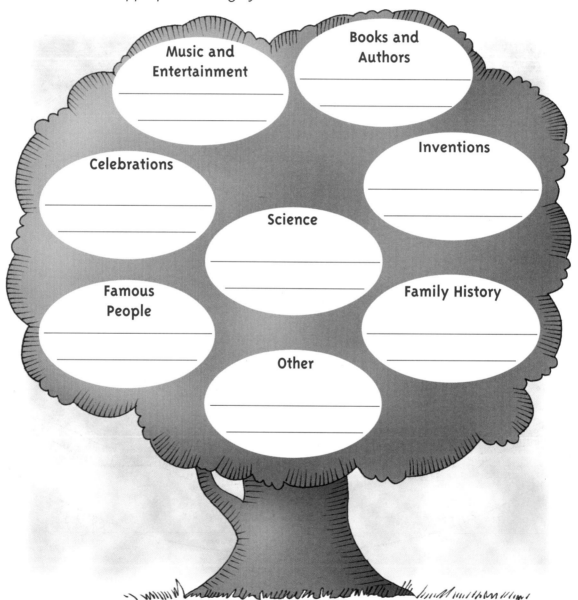

Music and Entertainment

Books and Authors

Celebrations

Inventions

Science

Famous People

Family History

Other

- I found three events that happened on my birthdate. Yes ☐ No ☐
- I used Chatterbox 2 for help. Yes ☐ No ☐
- This is where I found my information: _____ .

Write down some events that happened on the date you were born.

Students will write a rough draft of their texts.

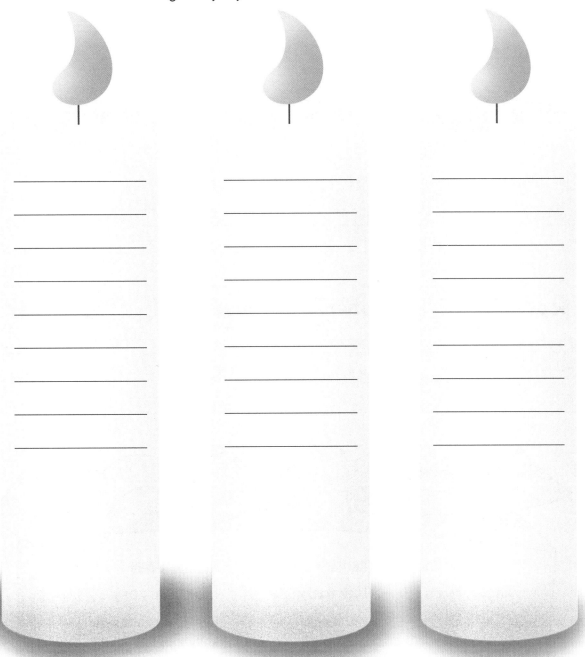

• **I presented the events that happened on my birthdate.**   Yes ☐   No ☐
• **I liked this unit.**   Yes ☐   No ☐

Special Events

▶ **Place each special event on the calendar.**
Students will match each event with its month.

January	February	March	April
New Year's Day	Valentine's Day	Easter, Holi, St. Patrick's Day	April Fool's Day, Easter

May	June	July	August
May Day, Mother's Day	Father's Day, Fête nationale,	Canada Day	August Moon Festival

September	October	November	December
Labour Day, Rosh Hoshanah	Diwali, Halloween	Diwali, Remembrance Day	Christmas, Hanukkah

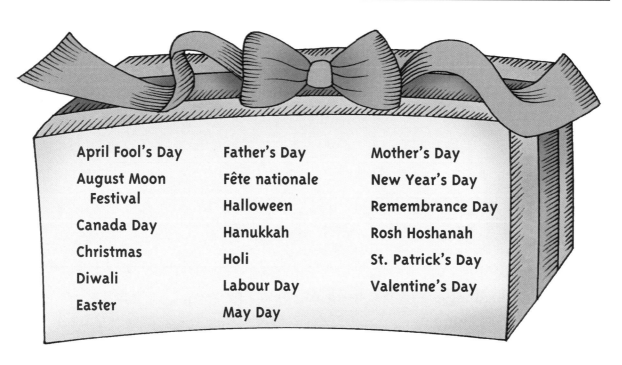

April Fool's Day
August Moon Festival
Canada Day
Christmas
Diwali
Easter

Father's Day
Fête nationale
Halloween
Hanukkah
Holi
Labour Day
May Day

Mother's Day
New Year's Day
Remembrance Day
Rosh Hoshanah
St. Patrick's Day
Valentine's Day

Unit 3

Words of Honour

Warm-up

▶ **Match the pictures with the sentences.**

▶ **Write the numbers on the blank lines.**

(a) The lion is the most popular animal in heraldry.

_____4_____

(b) Heraldry started in the Middle Ages in Europe.

_____1_____

(c) Nobles could give a coat of arms to a peasant.

_____6_____

(d) Many different signs and symbols are used in heraldry.

_____2_____

(e) A coat of arms on a shield identified soldiers.

_____5_____

(f) Different colours and metals are used on a coat of arms.

_____3_____

- **I worked well with my partners.**
  Always ☐   Most of the time ☐   Some of the time ☐   Never ☐
- **I used Chatterbox 6 for help.**   Yes ☐   No ☐

▶ Colour Gladwin's coat of arms according to the description in the story.

The coat of arms should be coloured as follows: gold background; blue tower; green dolphin; rainbow; blue candle. Colours: gold = generosity; blue = loyalty and truth; green = happiness, hope and joy; tower = safety; dolphin = charity and love; rainbow = good times after bad; candle = light and life; ivy leaves = strong friendship.

- **I understood the story.**
  All of it ☐   Most of it ☐   Some of it ☐   None of it ☐
- **I guessed the meaning of some words.**   Yes ☐   No ☐
- **I liked ☐ didn't like ☐ the story because** _____
  _____ .

Continued on next page

Activity 1 The Keeper (continued)

▶ Read the story.

▶ Answer the questions.

---

1. **Who was with the man?**
   The man was alone.

2. **What did he see in the distance?**
   He saw a village.

3. **Why didn't he know if he could reach the village?**
   The village was far away.

4. **Why did he pull the blanket over his head?**
   He was cold. / It was very cold.

---

1. **Where did the man go when he reached the village?**
   He went to an inn called The Royal Lion.

2. **How did the people greet him at The Royal Lion?**
   They closed the door in his face.

3. **How did the man feel?**
   He felt discouraged.

---

1. **What did the man do next?**
   He saw another inn, which was small, old and neglected.

2. **What did the innkeeper do?**
   She invited him inside.

3. **What did she give the man?**
   She gave him something to eat and drink.

4. **What did the peasants discover about this man?**
   They discovered that he was the King.

---

1. **What did the King give the innkeeper? Why?**
   The King gave the innkeeper a surname and a coat of arms because the innkeeper was kind and generous.

2. **What did the King decide to put on the coat of arms?**
   A gold background, a blue tower, a green dolphin, a rainbow, a blue candle, green ivy leaves, "Gladwin: The King's Friend," a motto.

Extension Activity

A New Beginning

► **Predict the beginning of the story "The Keeper."**

► **Answer the questions.**

Why was the king alone?

Answers will vary.

_____

_____

Where was he coming from?

Answers will vary.

_____

_____

What happened to the people he was with?

Answers will vary.

_____

_____

_____

Activity **2** What's in a Name?

▶ Read your text.

▶ Complete the chart with your partners.

Origin of Name	Examples
Father's name	Williamson, Davidson, MacDonald, McDonald, Fitzpatrick
Trade or occupation	Shepherd, Barber, Boucher, Mayor, Baxter, Farmer
Nickname	Smart, Good, Kennedy, Bonham (means "bon homme" or good man)
Location	Conway, London, Atwood, Bolton

▶ Read the list of names on page 25 in your book.

▶ Group the names by origin.

Father's name	Trade or occupation
Anderson, Fitzpatrick, MacDonald, Williamson	Boucher, Carpenter, Farmer, Knight

Nickname	Location
Bright, Little, Noble, Sharp	Barnes, Hill, Mountain, Woods

- **I paid attention to my partners.**
  Always ☐   Most of the time ☐   Some of the time ☐   Never ☐
- **I shared information with my partners.**   Yes ☐   No ☐
- **I used Chatterbox 11 for help.**   Yes ☐   No ☐

The Origin of My Name

▶ **Find out the meaning and origin of your family name.**

My family name is

_____ *Answers will vary.* _____

It comes from

_____ *Answers will vary.* _____

_____

_____

It means

_____ *Answers will vary.* _____

_____

_____

▶ Find the meaning of the objects and colours on Gladwin's coat of arms.

▶ Write why you think the King chose these objects and colours.

Object or Colour	Meaning	Reason
Gold	Generosity	The innkeeper showed generosity to the King.
Blue	Loyalty and truth	She was loyal.
Green	Happiness, hope, joy	She gave the King hope of survival.
Tower	Safety	She provided safety for the King.
Dolphin	Charity and love	She was charitable.
Candle	Light and life	She saved the King's life.
Ivy leaves	Strong friendship	There is now a strong friendship between the innkeeper and the King.

- **I discovered the meanings of the symbols.**
  All of them ☐   Most of them ☐   Some of them ☐   None of them ☐

SB 28

▶ **Invent your personal motto.**

Hear ye! Hear ye!

_____ 's

(your name)

motto will be:

Answers will vary.

_____

_____

- **I understood the mottoes.**
  All of them ☐   Most of them ☐   Some of them ☐   None of them ☐
- **I wrote my own motto with ☐ or without ☐ help.**

▶ Plan your personal coat of arms.

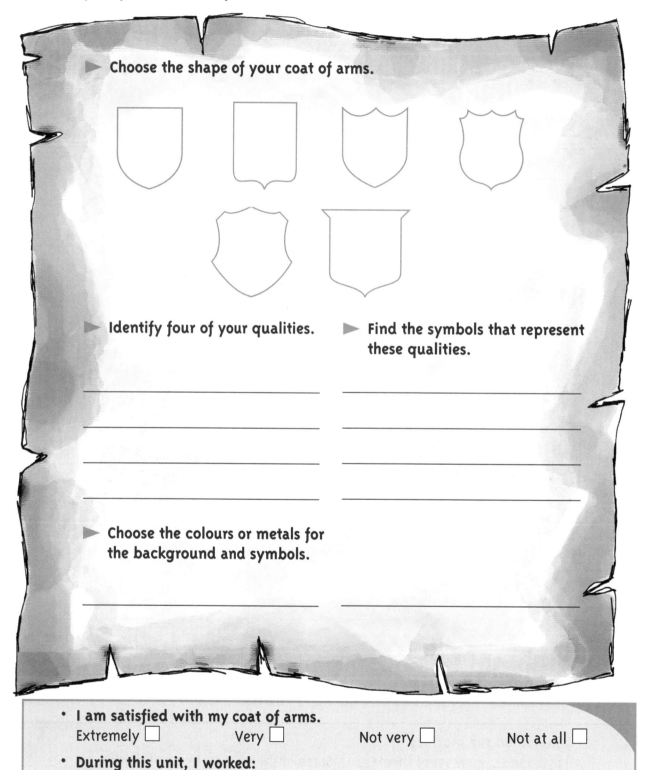

▶ Choose the shape of your coat of arms.

▶ Identify four of your qualities.

▶ Find the symbols that represent these qualities.

_____

_____

_____

_____

▶ Choose the colours or metals for the background and symbols.

_____

- **I am satisfied with my coat of arms.**
  Extremely ☐   Very ☐   Not very ☐   Not at all ☐
- **During this unit, I worked:**
  Very hard ☐   Moderately hard ☐   Not very hard ☐   Not hard at all ☐

Extension Activity

My Own Coat of Arms

► Find out if your family has a coat of arms.

► Draw a picture of it.

Pictures will vary.

Celebrating Celebrities

▶ **Think of a famous person you admire.**

▶ **Design a coat of arms for this person.**

*Students will design a coat of arms for a
famous person.*

▶ **Write down why you chose the symbols and colours for this person.**

Students will explain their choices.

Unit

4

Playing Around

▶ **Name as many toys as you can.**

▶ **Label the toys.**

kite

puppet

hula hoop

model kit

yo-yo

rocket

electric train

skateboard

board game

pogo stick

truck

teddy bear

- **I helped my partners find the names of the toys and games.** Yes ☐ No ☐
- **I was able to identify the toys and games.**
  All of them ☐   Most of them ☐   Some of them ☐   None of them ☐

Timeless Toys

▶ **Write the name of each item described in Otto's letter.**

▶ **Find the picture and write its letter in the appropriate place.**

▶ **Find a modern version for each item.**

	Item	Then	Now
1.	teddy bear	E	*Students will paste a modern version of the toy from a catalogue or flyer.*
2.	electric train	A	
3.	doll	D	
4.	yo-yo	C	
5.	board game	B	

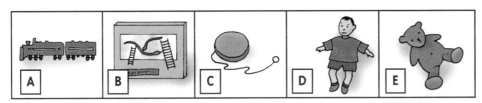

A   B   C   D   E

• **I named the items described in the letter.**
  All of them ☐   Most of them ☐   Some of them ☐   None of them ☐

• **I found the key words in the descriptions.**   Yes ☐   No ☐

• **I found a modern version for each toy.**   Yes ☐   No ☐

▶ Write the names of the toys that go in each toy box.

▶ Suggest some more toys for each toy box.

ABC blocks; hand puppet; jack-in-the-box; spinning top; teddy bear	*building blocks; doll's house; hand puppet; modelling clay; pogo stick; spinning top; teddy bear; teenage doll; yo-yo*
 **Toys for tots (ages 0 to 2)**	 **I'm a big kid now! (ages 2 to 5)**
building blocks; chemistry set; electric train; hula hoop; kite; model-boat kit; modelling clay; remote-control car; rocket; skateboard; teenage doll; yo-yo	*building blocks; chemistry set; electric train; kite; model-boat kit; remote-control car; rocket; skateboard; teddy bear*
 **Older kids like to play (ages 6 to 12)**	 **Really big kids like toys too! (age 12+)**

- **I worked well with my partners.**
  Always ☐   Most of the time ☐   Some of the time ☐   Never ☐
- **I spoke English during this activity.**
  Always ☐   Most of the time ☐   Some of the time ☐   Never ☐
- **I shared my opinion with my partners.**   Yes ☐   No ☐

▶ Listen to the ads.

▶ Put the pictures in order.

- **I understood the advertisements.**
  All of them ☐   Most of them ☐   Some of them ☐   None of them ☐
- **I was able to put the pictures in order.**   Yes ☐   No ☐

Something Old, Something New

▶ **With your partner, select a toy to remodel.**

We will remodel:

Students will choose a toy to remodel.

▶ **Make a sketch of your toy.**

Students will make a rough sketch of the toy they will remodel.

- • **I spoke English during this activity.**
  Always ☐   Most of the time ☐   Some of the time ☐   Never ☐
- • **I used Chatterbox 9 for help.**   Yes ☐   No ☐

▶ **Draw a picture of your new toy.**

Students will draw a picture of their new toys.

▶ **Write the advertisement to present your new toy.**

▶ **Remember to use:**

- an adjective to describe your product ☐
- an adjective ending in -able ☐
- an advertising expression ☐

Students will write an advertisement to present their new toys.

_____

_____

_____

- **I listened carefully to my classmates' presentations.**   Yes ☐   No ☐
- **I worked well with my partner.**
  Always ☐   Most of the time ☐   Some of the time ☐   Never ☐

Activity

What Am I?

▶ Read the clues.

▶ Guess which popular toy is being described.

1. These first appeared in North America in 1903.
   A child uses 730 of these before the age of ten.
   They come in 120 colours.

   crayons

2. Children played with these in Babylon in 2000 BC.
   They are usually decorated.
   They whistle when they turn.

   spinning tops

3. These were invented in China.
   There are four symbols on them.
   Each one represents one week of the year.

   playing cards

4. These were invented in 3000 BC.
   They were made of clay, stone, wood or glass.
   One of them is called a "shooter."

   marbles

Unit
5

Fear Files

Warm-up

► **Name some fears.**

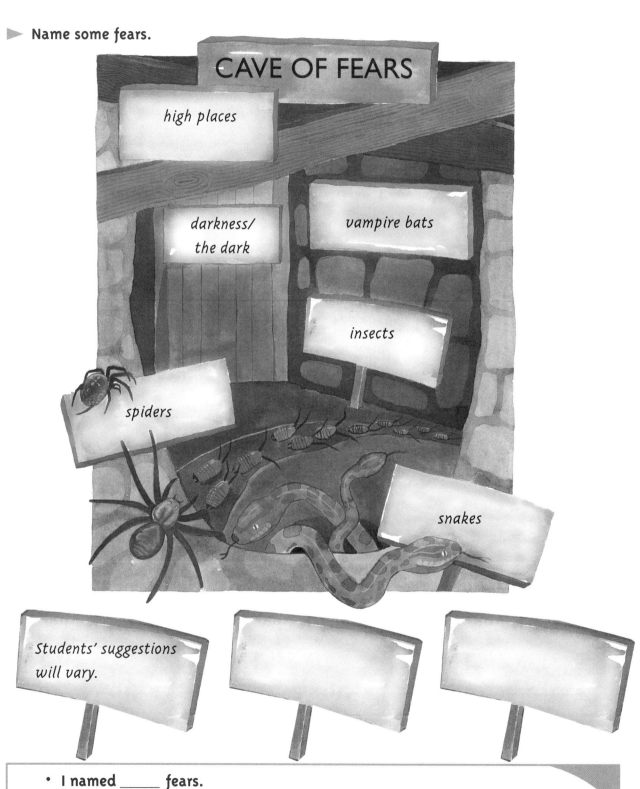

CAVE OF FEARS

high places

darkness/ the dark

vampire bats

insects

spiders

snakes

Students' suggestions will vary.

- **I named _____ fears.**
- **This activity was:**
  Very easy ☐   Easy ☐   Difficult ☐   Very difficult ☐

Activity 1 — The Physical Signs of Fear

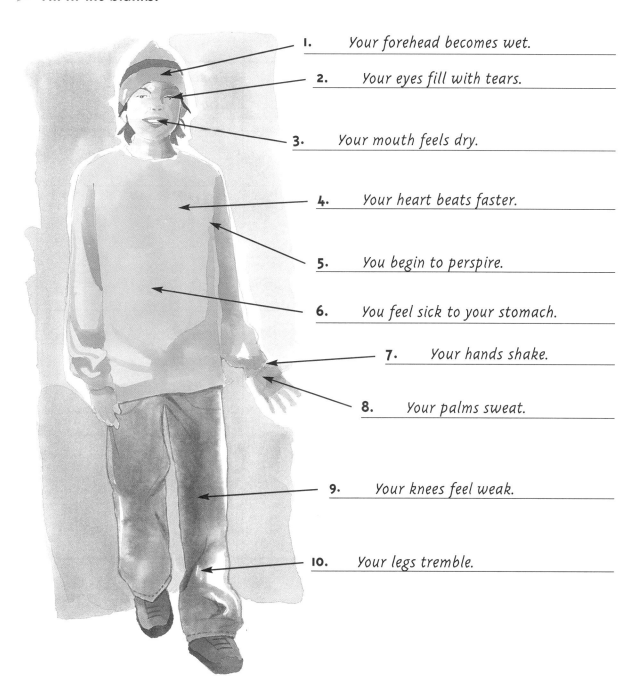

▶ Write what happens when you feel afraid.

▶ Fill in the blanks.

1. *Your forehead becomes wet.* _____

2. *Your eyes fill with tears.* _____

3. *Your mouth feels dry.* _____

4. *Your heart beats faster.* _____

5. *You begin to perspire.* _____

6. *You feel sick to your stomach.* _____

7. *Your hands shake.* _____

8. *Your palms sweat.* _____

9. *Your knees feel weak.* _____

10. *Your legs tremble.* _____

	Yes ☐ No ☐
• **I understood the text.**	Yes ☐ No ☐
• **I wrote down the physical signs of fear.**	
All of them ☐ Most of them ☐ Some of them ☐ None of them ☐	

Fear: A Report

► **Listen to the interviews.**

► **Complete the chart.**

Name	Age	Fear	Symptom	Solution
Floyd	14	bats	He shakes. He feels sick.	He goes inside as fast as he can.
Vivian	7	thunder	She gets scared. She cries.	She hides.
Helga	18	the dark	Her heart beats fast. Her legs shake.	She sleeps with a night light on.
Greg	32	elevators	His palms sweat. His hands tremble.	He uses the stairs when he can.

  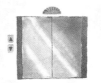 

- **I understood the interviews.**   Yes ☐   No ☐
- **I completed the chart with ☐ or without ☐ help.**

➤ **Write what happens when you feel afraid.**
➤ **Fill in the blanks.**

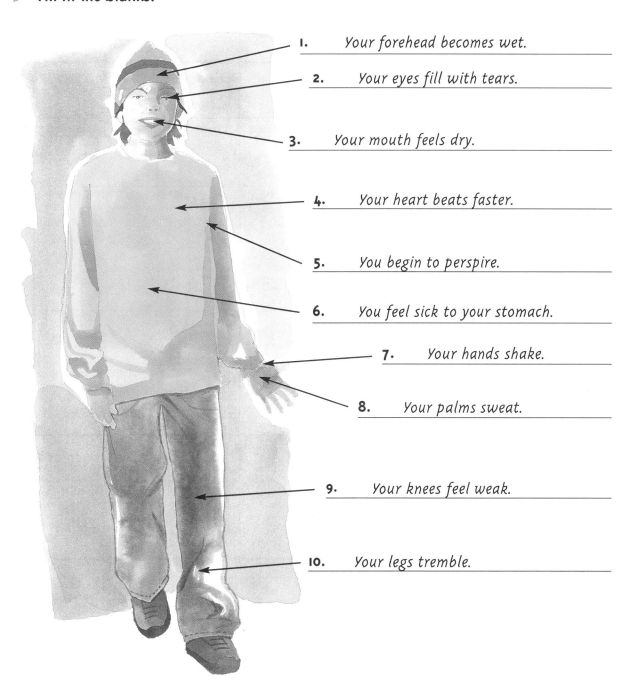

1. *Your forehead becomes wet.*

2. *Your eyes fill with tears.*

3. *Your mouth feels dry.*

4. *Your heart beats faster.*

5. *You begin to perspire.*

6. *You feel sick to your stomach.*

7. *Your hands shake.*

8. *Your palms sweat.*

9. *Your knees feel weak.*

10. *Your legs tremble.*

- **I understood the text.** Yes ☐ No ☐
- **I wrote down the physical signs of fear.**
  All of them ☐   Most of them ☐   Some of them ☐   None of them ☐

Activity 2 Fear: A Report

▶ Listen to the interviews.

▶ Complete the chart.

Name	Age	Fear	Symptom	Solution
Floyd	14	bats	He shakes. He feels sick.	He goes inside as fast as he can.
Vivian	7	thunder	She gets scared. She cries.	She hides.
Helga	18	the dark	Her heart beats fast. Her legs shake.	She sleeps with a night light on.
Greg	32	elevators	His palms sweat. His hands tremble.	He uses the stairs when he can.

- I understood the interviews.   Yes ☐   No ☐
- I completed the chart with ☐ or without ☐ help.

Activity 3 A Story of Fear

▶ Write your own version of the story.

▶ For each number, choose one of the options listed on the index card below.

Stories will vary.

The night was _____¹. I walked slowly
down the _____² road. My heart was
beating very fast. I was so _____³. Suddenly
I heard a sound. What was it? A _____⁴?
My foot hit something. It moved. _____!⁵
Oh, no! A _____⁶? I jumped. I tried
to _____⁷ but I couldn't. My _____⁸
were shaking. Then I saw the thing clearly. It was
_____⁹. Finally I ran away. I am so
afraid of _____¹⁰!

1. dark, stormy, rainy	6. snake, rat, tarantula
2. lonely, long, dark	7. scream, run, escape
3. afraid, scared, terrified	8. knees, hands, legs
4. bat, bear, wolf	9. ugly, enormous, angry
5. Look out! Watch out! Be careful!	10. skunks, squirrels, cats

- **I used Chatterbox 15 for help.**　　　　　Yes ☐　No ☐
- **I wrote my own story.**　　　　　　　　Yes ☐　No ☐
- **I am happy with the story I wrote.**
  Extremely ☐　　　Very ☐　　　Not very ☐　　　Not at all ☐

Extension Activity

Another Story of Fear

▶ **Read the story.**

The room was small and very dirty. Rats ran across the floor. The door was locked. I was alone. My hands started to shake. I saw a note on the table. It said, "Be careful! You are in danger!"

Suddenly I heard a noise behind me. I turned around and saw an enormous wolf. I began to scream. I was so afraid. Then I heard a voice shouting, "Wake up! It's time to go to school." Phew!

▶ **Now fill in the blanks to create a new story.**   *Stories will vary.*

The room was _____ and very _____.
_____ ran across the floor. The door was locked.
I was _____. _____ started to shake.
I saw a note on the table. It said, "_____ !
You are in danger!"

Suddenly I heard a _____ behind me. I turned
around and saw _____. I began
_____. I was so _____. Then I heard a
voice shouting, "Wake up! It's time to go to school." Phew!

Activity 4 Finding Fears

► Interview four people about their fears.

► Record your results on the chart.

Students will fill in the information they obtained from the four people they interviewed.

Name	Age	Fear	Symptom	Solution

- I interviewed _____ people.
- This activity was fun.   Yes ☐   No ☐

▶ **Plan your Cave of Fears on this page.**

Students will design their Cave of Fears, according to the results they obtained in their interviews.

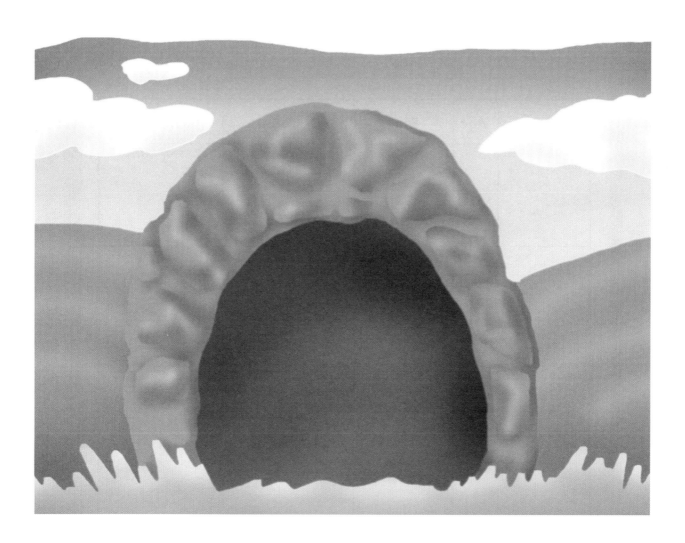

- **I spoke English during this activity.**
  Always ☐   Most of the time ☐   Some of the time ☐   Never ☐

- **I am satisfied with my work.**
  Extremely ☐   Very ☐   Not very ☐   Not at all ☐

A Circle of Fear

► Think of two other things you fear the most.
► Draw them in the circle below.
► Add them to your Cave of Fears.

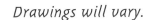

Drawings will vary.

My Scariest Things

► Look at the four categories.

► Write what scares you the most in each category.

Scariest movie:

Answers will vary.

_____

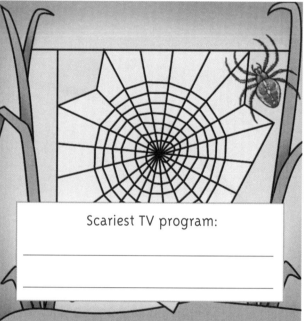

Scariest TV program:

_____

_____

Scariest book:

_____

_____

Scariest creature:

_____

_____

Unit
6

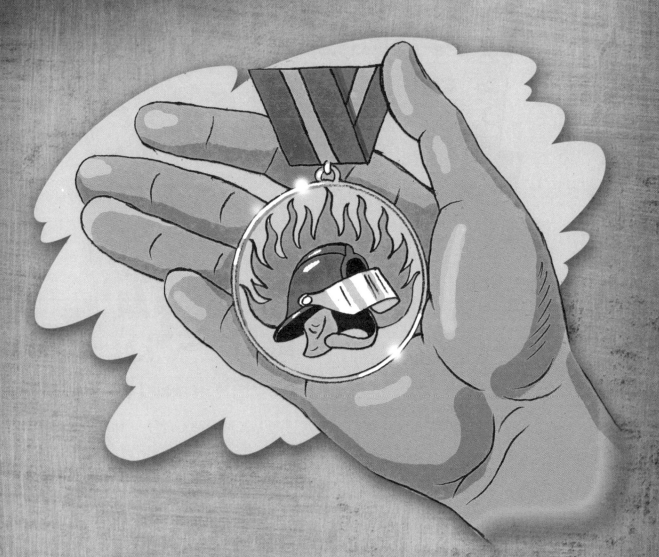

It Takes Courage

► **Identify the pictures that show acts of courage.**

2. Courageous ☑   Not courageous ☐

1. Courageous ☑   Not courageous ☐

4. Courageous ☑   Not courageous ☐

3. Courageous ☐   Not courageous ☑

► **Describe some other acts of courage.**

Answers will vary.

• **I understand what courage means.**	Yes ☐	No ☐
• **I can name some courageous actions.**	Yes ☐	No ☐

Down Under

▶ **Answer the questions before listening to the story.**

1. What is the title of the story? _____Down Under_____

2. Who are the main characters? _____Orpheus and Eurydice_____

3. Where does the story take place? _____Ancient Greece_____

4. What do you think the theme of the story is? *Answers will vary.*

   love ☐   recklessness ☐   courage ☐   honesty ☐

▶ **Listen to the first part of the story.**

▶ **Check off your answers.**

1. Orpheus and Eurydice got married.   True ✓   False ☐

2. Eurydice was bitten by a snake.   True ✓   False ☐

3. Eurydice immediately fell asleep.   True ☐   False ✓

4. Orpheus decided to bring Eurydice back from the
   World of the Dead.   True ✓   False ☐

▶ **Predict the ending of the story.** *Answers will vary.*

I think Orpheus:

— will be able to bring Eurydice back from the World of the Dead.   ☐

— won't be able to bring Eurydice back from the World of the Dead.   ☐

— won't be able to return from the World of the Dead.   ☐

— will meet another woman, fall in love and get married again.   ☐

Continued on next page

It Takes Courage

 **Down Under (continued)**

▶ Listen to the last part of the story.

▶ Write the names of the characters and state who they are.

	Orpheus	A musician
	Eurydice	Orpheus' wife
	Charon	Keeper of the River Styx
	Cerberus	A ferocious dog with three heads
	Hades	King of the World of the Dead

▶ Place the events in order.

  3   A. Orpheus decided to bring Eurydice back from the World of the Dead.

  8   B. Orpheus and Eurydice walked back through a dark tunnel.

  9   C. Orpheus heard a cry and turned to Eurydice, who disappeared forever.

  5   D. Orpheus charmed Cerberus and entered the World of the Dead.

  1   E. Orpheus and Eurydice loved each other and decided to get married.

  6   F. Orpheus convinced Hades to let Eurydice return to the Land of the Living.

  7   G. Orpheus promised not to look at Eurydice until they were out of the World of the Dead.

  4   H. Orpheus crossed the River Styx after charming Charon.

  2   I. On their wedding day, Eurydice stepped on a poisonous snake and died instantly.

- **I was able to identify the characters, setting and theme of the story.**   Yes ☐   No ☐
- **I understood the main events of the story.**
  All of them ☐   Most of them ☐   Some of them ☐   None of them ☐

Activity 2 — A Model of Courage

▶ **Answer the questions.**

Who is this person?
Chantal Petitclerc

Why did she begin to swim every day?
to stay in good physical shape

What sport did she discover?
wheelchair racing

What has she won?
gold, silver and bronze medals

Which competitions has she participated in?
marathons, Paralympic Games, Commonwealth games

▶ **Write why you think she is a hero.**
Answers will vary.

• **I understood the text about Chantal Petitclerc.**
All of it ☐   Most of it ☐   Some of it ☐   None of it ☐

► **Match each letter with its solution.**

Newville Elementary Monthly News

Tell your fears to Dr Fear

Dear Dr Fear,
After school my friends are teaching me tricks to do on my bicycle. Yesterday I fell. Now I am afraid to get hurt again. What should I do?

Dear Dr Fear,
All the girls in my class are getting tattoos. I think they look silly. It's not what I want to do. But I want to be like the other kids. Can I still be cool without a tattoo?

Dear Dr Fear,
I have to wear glasses. I am too shy to wear them. I always carry them in my schoolbag.

The problem is: I can't see without them. Next week I have a big test. Will my friends laugh at me if I wear my glasses?

6

Dear Friend,
Courage comes in many forms. It takes courage to believe in your friends. They will not laugh at you if they are true friends. They will understand. Write your test. Wear your glasses. Your eyes are very important.

Dear Friend,
You are right to worry about getting hurt again. Wear a helmet, elbow pads and knee pads. Don't be reckless. Be safe! Your friends may follow your example.

Dear Friend,
Stand up for what you want. Don't be afraid to be different. Be you!

7

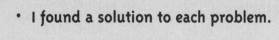

• **I found a solution to each problem.** Yes ☐ No ☐

Nicholas's Problem

▶ **Read the letter to Dr Fear.**

Dear Dr Fear,

I have a big problem. I like a girl in my class and I want her to like me. Her name is Yulan. She's an excellent swimmer. Last week she won a bronze medal.

Next week our class is going to the pool. I don't know how to swim and I'm afraid of the water. Yulan will surely laugh at me. This will ruin my chances with her. What should I do?

Sincerely,

Nicholas

▶ **Answer the questions.**

1. What is the girl's name? _____ *Yulan* _____

2. What is she good at? _____ *swimming* _____

3. What is Nicholas's problem? *He doesn't know how to swim. / He's afraid* *of the water.*

4. What should Nicholas do? *Answers will vary.*

a) Pretend he can swim and dive into the deep end.

b) Pretend he has a cold and sit on a bench near the pool.

c) Tell Yulan he is afraid of the water.

d) Ask Yulan to teach him how to swim.

▶ **Write a letter in response to Nicholas.**

Answers will vary.

_____

_____

_____

_____

▶ **Read the nominations.**

Sheila MacDonald

My grandmother's husband died when she was thirty-four years old. She had nine young children to support. She decided to manage my grandfather's store. Everyone was against the idea. This decision took a lot of courage. She raised her family and worked full-time. She overcame all the obstacles and became a successful business woman.

My grandmother Sheila MacDonald

Pamela Green-Ladouceur

My younger sister has a learning disability. She has trouble speaking and writing. Her dream was to become a baker. She was sure she could succeed. She studied hard and never gave up. She finally received her diploma. She now works in an excellent restaurant and makes the best cheesecake in town.

My sister: Pamela Green-Ladouceur

Vijay Musharraf and King

My cousin trained his dog King very well. Last summer, King saved me from drowning. I was swimming in a river with a strong current. Suddenly I couldn't get back to shore. My cousin told King to go and get me. King immediately jumped into the water. I held on to his neck as he swam back to shore. King and my cousin are terrific!

My cousin Vijay and his dog King

Continued on next page

William Hunter

My father is a firefighter. He has to take many risks. He often has to enter buildings that are on fire. Every time there is a fire, my dad hopes that there won't be any victims. Sometimes it's too late and some people die. This makes my dad very sad. I'm very proud of my father because he has saved many lives.

Sheila MacDonald: grandmother; sexism. She became a successful business woman. Vijay and King: cousin; drowning. They saved me from drowning. Pamela Green-Ladouceur: younger sister; learning disability. She became a baker and got a good job. William Hunter: father; takes risks. He has saved many lives.

▶ **Decide who should receive the medal.**

The winner of the medal is ___*Answers will vary.*_____ because _____

_____ .

* **My presentation of the nominee was:**
  Excellent ☐   Very good ☐   Not very good ☐   Not good at all ☐
* **I used Chatterbox 6 for help in the group discussion.**   Yes ☐   No ☐

▶ Write some facts about a person you admire.

▶ Choose someone you admire. Find some facts about this person.

What?

Answers will vary.

_____
_____
_____
_____

When?

_____
_____
_____
_____

Who?

_____
_____
_____
_____

Where?

_____
_____
_____
_____

Why?

_____
_____
_____
_____

Continued on next page

▶ **Write the draft of your text about your hero.**

Texts will vary.

- **The text I wrote about my hero was:**
  Excellent ☐   Very good ☐   Not very good ☐   Not good at all ☐
- **I am satisfied with the presentation I gave about my hero.**
  Extremely ☐   Very ☐   Not very ☐   Not at all ☐

They Made a Difference

► Read the descriptions.
► Match each description with its picture.

1. Roberta Bondar

2. Terry Fox

3. Lucille Teasdale-Corti

4. Jean Vanier

At the age of 18, he discovered that he had cancer in his right leg. In 1980, he ran across Canada on a journey he called the Marathon of Hope. He raised over $24 million for cancer research. __2__

After a brilliant career in the army, he founded a centre to take care of adults with developmental disabilities. Built in 1964, the centre was called L'Arche. There are now over one hundred of these centres around the world. __4__

She joined the Canadian Space Program in 1983. In 1992, she flew on the space shuttle Discovery to perform experiments. She was the first Canadian woman in space. __1__

She graduated from Université de Montréal in 1955. She became one of the first woman surgeons in Québec. She and her husband built a modern hospital and a school of nursing in Uganda. __3__

Unit 7

Beat the Record

Name Those Records!

▶ **Write the record beside the picture.**

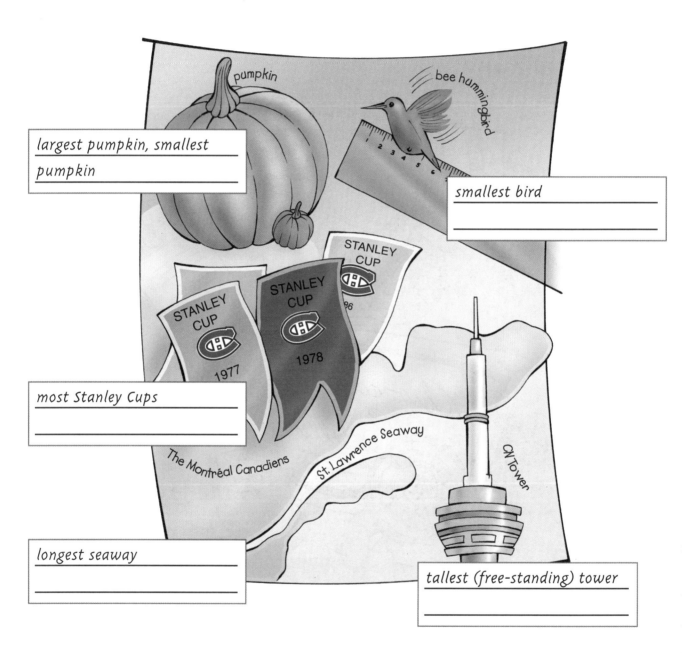

largest pumpkin, smallest
pumpkin _____

smallest bird _____
_____

most Stanley Cups _____
_____

longest seaway _____
_____

tallest (free-standing) tower _____
_____

• **I identified _____ world records.**

Kids on Record

SB 59

► Complete the following records.

Event	Record holder
Fastest crossword team	*Greta & Daniel*
Loudest whistle	*Abdul*
Biggest bubble	*Rémi*
Longest list	*Miranda*

► Survey your classmates and add their suggestions to this list.

► Find the record holder in your group.

Event	Record holder
Shortest pencil	*Answers will vary.*
Most knots in a shoelace	
Most CDs at home	

- I made a list of _____ records with my partner.
- I spoke English during this activity.
  Always ☐   Most of the time ☐   Some of the time ☐   Never ☐

Extension Activity

Who Did What?

► Write about the record holders.

► Complete the sentences.

Remi _____ _blew_ _____

the biggest bubble.

Miranda _____ _wrote_ _____

the longest list.

Abdul _____ _has_ _____

the loudest whistle.

Greta and Daniel _____

finished _____ their puzzle first.

For the Record

▶ **Find some more record holders.**

▶ **Ask your classmates these questions.**

▶ **Identify the record holder in each category.**

- How many pets do you have?
- How many telephones are there in your house?
- How many brothers do you have?
- How many sisters do you have?
- How many aunts and uncles do you have?

> most pets
> most telephones
> most brothers
> most sisters
> most aunts and uncles

Name	Pets	Telephones	Brothers	Sisters	Aunts and uncles
Students will interview their classmates and record their answers. They will then identify which classmate holds the record in each category.					

Activity 2 Set Your Own Record!

SB 60

▶ **Record your partners' results.** *Students will record their partners' results.*

Name	Time	Rank

▶ **Make a bar graph to show the results.**

Students will make a bar graph showing the results for their events.

• I helped my partners make a bar graph.   Yes ☐   No ☐
• I spoke English during this activity.   Yes ☐   No ☐

66   sixty-six

Unit 7

©**ERPI** Please do not photocopy this page.

Activity 3 — Plan Your Event

▶ Complete the planning form.

Planning Form

Group members: *Answers will vary.*

Event:

Materials required:

Rules:

- I helped make the rules for an event.   Yes ☐   No ☐
- I used Chatterbox 5 for help.   Yes ☐   No ☐

©ERPI Please do not photocopy this page.

Beat the Record

Activity 4 Ready, Steady, Go!

▶ **Plan what you will write on the certificate.**

Students will plan what to write on the certificate.

**Beat-the-Record
Certificate**

To: _____

For: _____

From: _____

Congratulations!

- **I used Chatterbox ɪ for help.**   Yes ☐   No ☐
- **I participated in _____ events.**
- **My favourite event was:** _____.

Wrap-up

▶ Complete the following checklist.

▶ Copy it and add it to your section of the Class Record Book.

Our Team

Students will check off the items to be included in the Class Record Book.

Component	✓
Planning form	
List of participants:	
Bar graph	
Name of record holder:	

- **During this unit, I worked:**
  Very hard ☐   Hard ☐   Not very hard ☐   Not hard at all ☐

World Records

▶ Look for world records on the Internet or in library books.

▶ Start with these and add others.

1. The tallest totem pole (Canada):
   the Spirit of Lekwammen in Victoria, British Columbia

2. The most Oscars:
   Walt Disney won 26 Oscars between 1932 and 1969.

3. The biggest spider:
   the Goliath bird-eating spider of the rainforests of Surinam, Guyana and
   French Guiana

4. The highest waterfall:
   Angel Falls in Venezuela

5. The largest shopping centre:
   the West Edmonton Mall in Alberta

6. The youngest author:
   Dennis Vollmer of Oklahoma was six years old when he wrote and illustrated Joshua
   Disobeys. _It was published in 1989._

7. _Note: some of these answers may change over time._

8. _Students will add other world records._

Unit
8

Celebrating the World

Around the World

▶ Trace Paul and Paulette's journey on the map.

▶ Draw a line from country to country.

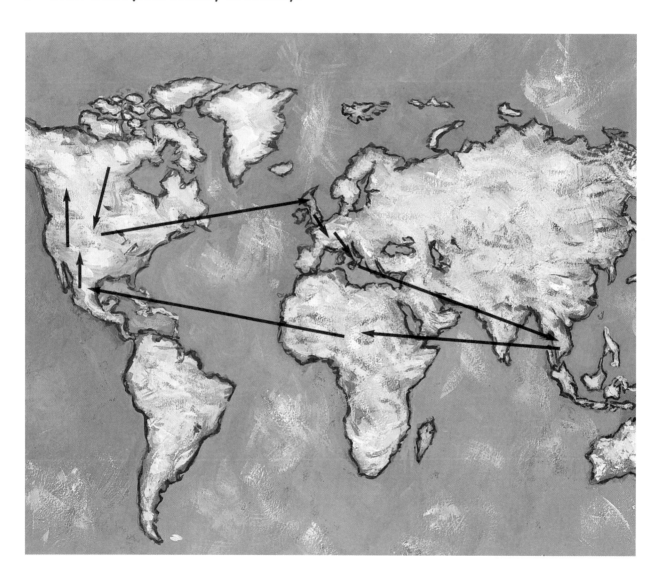

- I identified _____ places on the brochures.
- I named the celebrations.   Yes ☐   No ☐
- I was able to trace Paul and Paulette's journey on the map.   Yes ☐   No ☐

Activity 1 — May Day in England

▶ **Write the sentence that describes each picture.**

There is tall pole with many long
coloured ribbons.

People wear hats with flowers
on them.

The girls wear headbands decorated
with flowers.

A group of men called Morris dancers
perform a traditional dance.

• **I found a sentence describing each picture.**	Yes ☐	No ☐
• **I used Chatterbox 12 for help.**	Yes ☐	No ☐

Extension Activity

Scrambled Countries

▶ Unscramble the letters to discover the names of some countries.

1. MAEIVTN	V	I	E	T	N	A	M
2. COXMIE	M	E	X	I	C	O	
3. NACIH	C	H	I	N	A		
4. NIIAD	I	N	D	I	A		
5. NAADCA	C	A	N	A	D	A	
6. YTILA	I	T	A	L	Y		
7. ECNFRA	F	R	A	N	C	E	
8. ANGENLD	E	N	G	L	A	N	D

Activity 2 — A Day in Vietnam

▶ Place the postcards in order.

▶ Write a brief description of each postcard.

Descriptions will vary.

_____ _____ _____
_____ _____ _____
_____ _____ _____
_____ _____ _____
_____ _____ _____

▶ Draw another picture about the festival in Vietnam.

▶ Write a brief description of your picture.

Drawings will vary.

Descriptions will vary.
_____
_____
_____
_____

- **I found the key words in Paulette and Paul's letter.**
  All of them ☐   Most of them ☐   Some of them ☐   None of them ☐
- **I found the letter _____ to understand.**
  Very easy ☐   Easy ☐   Difficult ☐   Very difficult ☐

Activity 3 — Fun in Mexico

► Read the text that Paulette and Paul wrote.

► Decide which pictures they should put in their souvenir album.

► Write the number of the picture in the square.

2	5

Our photos

December

Mexico! What a wonderful place! We arrived just at the beginning of the Posadas. This is a celebration that lasts nine days. Every evening there is a parade. The parades are for the children but adults join in too.

At the end of the parade, the children try to break a piñata with a stick. The children are all blindfolded. It's fun to watch them but it's more fun to try to smash the piñata.

Piñatas are made from papier mâché, clay or cardboard. They come in many shapes such as animals or stars. They are full of special treats like candies, fruit, nuts and little toys. Next year we're going to make our own piñata at home.

- **I chose some pictures to put in the souvenir album.**   Yes ☐   No ☐
- **I found the text about Mexico _____ to understand.**
  Very easy ☐   Easy ☐   Difficult ☐   Very difficult ☐

My Piñata

► **Choose one of the recipes below and make your own piñata.**

Students will make their own piñatas.

Recipe 1. The Balloon and Paste Piñata

Materials required:
1 large balloon
newspaper
flour
water
paints
adhesive tape

Instructions:
- Blow up the balloon.
- Mix the flour and water to make a paste.
- Tear newspaper into strips.
- Cover the strips in paste.
- Cover the balloon with the newspaper strips.
- Let dry.
- Decorate.
- Cut an opening in the top of the piñata and fill with candies.
- Use adhesive tape to close the top of the piñata.

Recipe 2. The Paper Bag Piñata

Materials required:
3 large paper bags
Paint

Directions:
- Put the three bags one inside the other.
- Paint the outside with white water-based paint.
- Decorate the bag.
- Fill with candies and small toys.
- Tie the top of the bag with string.

Activity 4 Kwanzaa in the United Sates

▶ **Write your own invitation.**

Students will plan what to write on their invitations.

Come celebrate with us!

What?

When?

Who?

Why?

Where?

- **I understand what Kwanzaa is about.**   Yes ☐   No ☐
- **I wrote my own invitation with ☐ or without ☐ help.**

► **Use this form to plan your scrapbook.**

► **Complete the information about your choice of festival or celebration.**

My Plan

Students will plan what they will put in their scrapbooks. They will also write a rough draft of their texts.

Name of festival or celebration:

_____

Country where it takes place: _____

When it takes place: _____

What I will put on the cover of my scrapbook: _____

_____

_____

Pictures to put in my scrapbook: _____

_____

Web sites I visited for information: _____

_____

Draft of my text: _____

_____

_____

_____

Who helped me edit my text: _____

What I will put on the cover of my invitation: _____

_____

- **I prepared a scrapbook about** _____.
- **I am satisfied with my scrapbook.**
  Extremely ☐   Very ☐   Not very ☐   Not at all ☐

Invent a Celebration

▶ **Invent a special celebration.**

▶ **Use form A as a model.**

▶ **Use form B to write your plan.**

FORM A

What will the day be called? Freedom Day

What will it celebrate? The first day of summer vacation

When will it take place? June 25

What special activities will occur on this day?

Children will have a parade. They will go to the swimming pool on their bikes,

skateboards or rollerblades. There will be a barbecue and fireworks at night.

Everyone will wear a headband with a special symbol. Parents will give their

children a summer gift, like a new swimsuit or bike helmet.

What special symbol will represent your day? A flag with a bird flying out of a cage

---

FORM B

What will the day be called? *Answers will vary.*

What will it celebrate? _____

When will it take place? _____

What special activities will occur on this day?

_____

_____

_____

_____

What special symbol will represent your day? _____

Unit
9

Forever Friends

Hand in Hand

▶ **Choose a hand gesture.**

▶ **Draw the contour of your hand gesture.**

Drawings will vary.

▶ **Listen to your teacher.**

▶ **Write the information on your handprint.**

Students will write their names, one of their qualities, their best friend's name, one of her or his qualities, and one activity they like to do together.

- • **I learned something new about my partners.**
  All of them ☐   Most of them ☐   Some of them ☐   None of them ☐
- • **I used Chatterbox 10 for help.**   Yes ☐   No ☐

Extension Activity

Give Us a Hand!

► Work with your partners to invent a team handshake or signal.

► Draw your handshake or signal.

My partners are:

_____

_____

_____

Our handshake or signal is:

Students will write their partners' names and draw their team handshake or signal.

 The Homecoming

▶ **Put the events in order.**

| 4 | The friends decorate the house and wait for Henry's wife to return. |

| 1 | Lori meets Old Man Pettigrew and sees a photograph of his wife. |

| 5 | Lori learns that Mrs Pettigrew is dead and that the friends pretend she is coming home. |

| 2 | Meg comes to visit Mr Pettigrew and he tells her about the letter he received. |

| 3 | Joe and Henry plan a welcome-home party for Henry's wife. |

▶ **Write each sentence in the appropriate box.**

First, *Lori meets Old Man Pettigrew and sees a photograph of his wife.*

↓

Next, *Meg comes to visit Mr Pettigrew and he tells her about the letter he received.*

↓

Then, *Joe and Henry plan a welcome-home party for Henry's wife.*

↓

After that, *the friends decorate the house and wait for Henry's wife to return.*

↓

Finally, *Lori learns that Mrs Pettigrew is dead and that the friends pretend she is coming home.*

- **I enjoyed the play** *The Homecoming.* Yes ☐   No ☐
- **I thought the text was:**
  Very easy ☐   Easy ☐   Difficult ☐   Very difficult ☐

 **ctivity 2** | **Quite a Character!**

▶ **Choose one character from the play.**

▶ **Describe that character.**

Name of the Play:

Character's Name:

Lori (adult)

Description:

mature, reflective

Lori (young): young, helpful, happy, surprised. She worked for Mr Pettigrew. She met Mr Pettigrew's friends. She learns about friendship. She helped decorate the house.

What she or he did:

She tells the story and explains what friendship is all about.

Henry: old, sad, calm, lonely, nervous. He told Lori about his wife. He read the letter from her.

Agnes: old, loyal, quiet, calm, gentle, kind. She visited Henry. She decorated the house.

Joe: old, loyal, bright, happy, kind. He planned the welcome-home party. He decorated the house.

Meg: old, loyal, strong, confident, sensitive. She visited Henry. She asked him if he had any news from his wife. She cried. She decorated the house.

- **I described this character in the play:** _____ .
- **I spoke English with my partners.**
  Always ☐   Most of the time ☐   Some of the time ☐   Never ☐

▶ **Study your lines.**

▶ **Practise your part.**

▶ **Complete the sentences.**

Students will note down some tips to remember while rehearsing their parts.

I will play the part of _____ .

Some things I need to remember are _____

_____

Some words I find difficult are _____

_____

I need to practise _____ .

- **When I practised my part, I worked:**
  Very hard ☐   Moderately hard ☐   Not very hard ☐   Not hard at all ☐
- **I used Chatterbox 1 for help.**   Yes ☐   No ☐

Activity 4 Opening Night

▶ Design a program for your performance.
▶ Write the information for your program.

Students will write the information for their programs.

Characters:

_____

_____

_____

_____

_____

Cast of Characters:

_____

_____

_____

_____

_____

_____

_____

_____

_____

_____

Performance:

Date: _____

Time: _____

Place: _____

- I used Chatterbox 8 for help. Yes ☐ No ☐
- I helped my partners design a program for our performance. Yes ☐ No ☐

Wrap-up

► **Plan your performance of the play *The Homecoming*.**

Students will plan the details of their performance.

Choose the format for your performance. _____

_____

We will have music. Yes ☐   No ☐

We will use props.   Yes ☐   No ☐

The props we need are _____ .

_____

We will have costumes. Yes ☐   No ☐

We will bring _____ .

_____

• **During this unit, I worked:**
  Very hard ☐   Moderately hard ☐   Not very hard ☐   Not hard at all ☐

Extension Activity

My Review

► Write a review of *The Homecoming*.

THE HOMECOMING:

A new play comes to town!

Students will write a review about the play The Homecoming.

Mystery Word

▶ Find the words in the puzzle.

▶ Then find the mystery word.

N	C	G	M	A	R	G	O	R	P
A	H	N	E	P	A	R	T	I	E
R	A	I	P	O	R	P	H	S	R
R	R	T	L	T	I	S	I	E	F
A	A	T	A	R	D	T	C	N	O
T	C	E	N	C	A	T	I	R
O	T	S	E	A	S	G	I	L	M
R	E	I	R	T	G	E	R	E	A
W	R	P	N	I	A	T	R	U	C
F	A	U	D	I	E	N	C	E	T

ACT   CURTAIN   PART   PRACTISE   SCRIPT
AUDIENCE   FRIENDSHIP   PERFORM   PROGRAM   SETTING
CAST   LINES   PLACE   PROP   STAGE
CHARACTER   NARRATOR

Mystery word: P E T T I G R E W

Who am I? *the old man in* The Homecoming

Unit 10

Signs of the Times

 **Warm-up**

Yesterday and Tomorrow

► Describe what you see.

► Use this page for your notes.

Possible answers: a boy running with a dog; a girl playing with her doll; a man delivering mail; a man playing a musical instrument

_____

_____

_____

Possible answers: two children on flying skateboards, two children listening to music; a strange airplane, music coming out of a child's pocket

_____

_____

_____

- **I found** _____ **different signs on the cover page.**
- **I described the pictures during the warm-up activity.** Yes ☐ No ☐

Describe today's fashions.

Draw or paste pictures of these fashions.

Today's Fashions

Headgear

_____
_____
_____
_____

Footwear

_____
_____
_____
_____

Coats and jackets

_____
_____
_____
_____
_____

Students will draw or paste pictures of contemporary fashions and then write a brief description of each item.

Pants and skirts

_____
_____
_____
_____
_____

- **The texts were _____ to read.**
  Very easy ☐   Easy ☐   Difficult ☐   Very difficult ☐
- **I am happy with my fashion page.**   Yes ☐ No ☐

# Extension Activity

In Fashion

► Look at the topics below.

► Find illustrations of this year's models from magazines, catalogues or flyers.

► Glue your favourites on the page.

In the year
_____

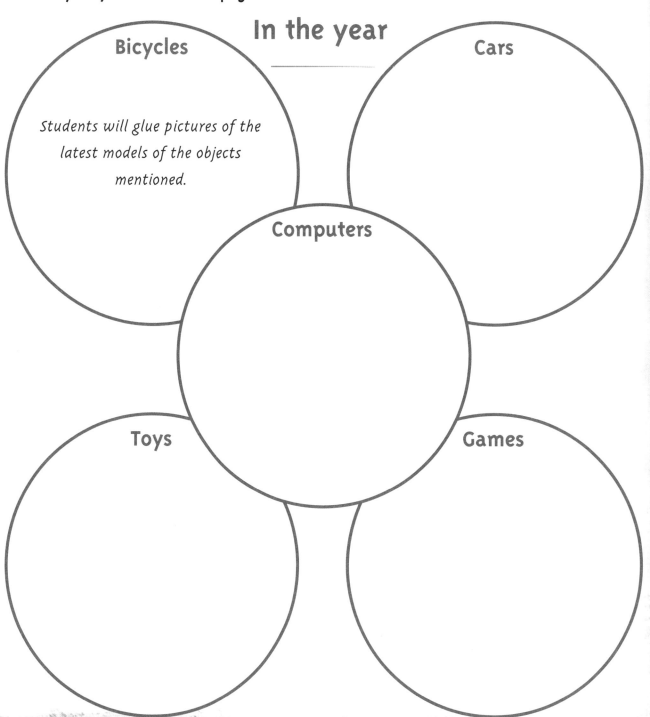

Bicycles

Cars

Students will glue pictures of the latest models of the objects mentioned.

Computers

Toys

Games

Activity 2 — Signs and Sounds

▶ Read the reviews and answer the questions.

What are the names of the two groups?

The Hummingbirds   The Asteroid Ants

Which eras do they represent?

the 1960s   the 2060s

Why are these groups popular with young people?

They play great music from the 1960s: steady beat, great guitar sound and fabulous lyrics.

They play modern electronic music based on music from the past such as rap and rock 'n' roll.

Which group would you like to hear? Why?

Answers will vary.

Which group(s) of today do you like? Why?

Answers will vary.

- **I answered the questions about the music groups on the handout.**
  All of them ☐   Most of them ☐   Some of them ☐   None of them ☐
- **I used Chatterbox 8 for help.**   Yes ☐   No ☐

Activity 3 Sign Up for Fun

▶ Listen to the conversations.

▶ List the activities mentioned.

PAST • PAST

go to the park; play baseball; made a model car; watch TV

FUTURE • FUTURE • FUTURE • FUTURE • FUTURE • FUTURE • FUTURE • FUTURE • FUTURE • FUTURE • FUTURE • FUTURE • FUTURE • FUTURE • FUTURE • FUTURE • FUTURE

hover-ski; go to a virtual park; go time travelling

- I was able to name _____ activities.

- The conversations on the recording were _____ to understand.
  Very easy ☐   Easy ☐   Difficult ☐   Very difficult ☐

Activity 4 — Signs of Technology

▶ **Read the magazine articles and complete the charts.**

Features: First models were black, square, made of heavy-duty plastic. Later models: different colours and shapes, made of lighter plastic

Users: found in businesses, phone booths. Later in homes: adults, teenagers and even children

Operation: electricity; rotary dial; push buttons on a keypad

---

Features: Digital; cordless; portable; different colours and shapes; small and compact

Users: everybody

Operation: push buttons on a keypad

Features: microcircuits integrated into helmets

Users: everybody

Operation: voice commands

- **I spoke English with my partner.**
  Always ☐   Most of the time ☐   Some of the time ☐   Never ☐

- **I wrote down information about the three types of telephones.**
  Yes ☐   No ☐

SB 91

▶ **Use this questionnaire to plan your presentation.**
Answers will vary.

• What four categories will there be on our sign?

_____

• Who will present each part?

Category: _____	Category: _____
Presenter: _____	Presenter: _____
Category: _____	Category: _____
Presenter: _____	Presenter: _____

• What Web sites can we visit for information? What keywords can we use?

_____

_____

• What pictures should we look for?

_____

_____

• What kind of audio or video material can we use?

_____

• What other material do we need?

_____

• Who will bring what?

_____

_____

• **During the wrap-up, I worked:**
Extremely hard ☐ Very hard ☐ Not very hard ☐ Not hard at all ☐

©ERPI Please do not photocopy this page.

My Sign

▶ Create your personal sign.

▶ Choose one of these designs: a licence plate, a key ring, a bookplate or a sign for your bedroom door.

Students will each design a personal sign. The designs here are suggestions only.

Continued on next page

 **My Sign (continued)**

▶ **Use this space to plan your design and write your text.**

Designs and texts will vary.

Unit
11

The Forgetting Stone

A Story for Everyone

▶ Place each book in the appropriate category.

▶ Say what kind of story you prefer.

Science fiction

Jupiter: Flight IV

Biography

Laura Secord:
Her Story

Mystery

The Mystery of
Nob Hill

Adventure

Lightning:
A Rodeo Champion

Fantasy

A Witch's Wish

Horror

Horrible Tales from
Tanglewood Forest

My favourite type of story is: *Students will indicate the literary genres they prefer.*

- • I identified the different types of stories shown on the book covers.
  All of them ☐   Most of them ☐   Some of them ☐   None of them ☐
- • I used correct capitalization when I wrote the titles.   Yes ☐   No ☐

Extension Activity

My Bookmark

► Make a bookmark that shows the kind of story you prefer.

Students will design a bookmark illustrating the kind of story they prefer.

Extension Activity

Summer Reading Chart

► Keep a chart of the books you read during your summer vacation.

Date:	*Students can use this chart to keep track of their summer reading.*		
Title:			
Author:			
Type of story:			
Thumbs up:	👍	👍	👍
Thumbs down:	👎	👎	👎

Date:			
Title:			
Author:			
Type of story:			
Thumbs up:	👍	👍	👍
Thumbs down:	👎	👎	👎

Georgia's Discovery

> **Answer the questions.**

1. What does Georgia like and dislike?

   chocolate ice cream, cats, rocks and magazines; black jujubes, horse and thunderstorms

2. What does she hate?

   school

3. What does she hope for?

   to do well in school

4. Who is the man in the picture?

   her teacher

5. What did Georgia step on?

   a stone

> **Check off the correct sentence on each stepping stone.**

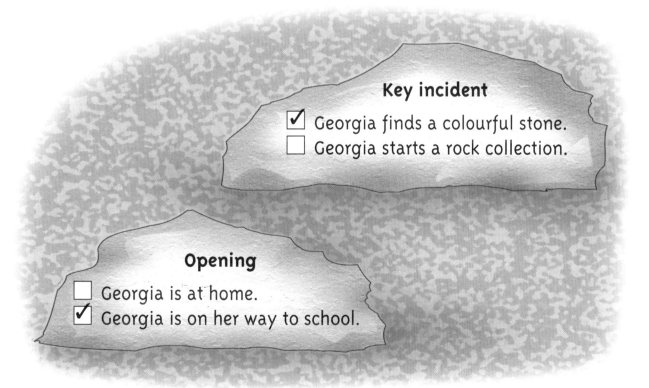

Key incident

☑ Georgia finds a colourful stone.
☐ Georgia starts a rock collection.

Opening

☐ Georgia is at home.
☑ Georgia is on her way to school.

Continued on next page

 **Georgia's Discovery** (continued)

Complete the chart with information about Georgia and yourself.

Georgia	Me
likes . . .	**I like . . .**
chocolate ice cream, cats, rocks and magazines	*Students will write some facts about themselves.*
dislikes . . .	**I dislike . . .**
black jujubes, horses and thunderstorms	
hates . . .	**I hate . . .**
school	
wants . . .	**I want . . .**
to do well in school and to do something she can be proud of	

• **I understood the first part of the story.**
  All of it ☐   Most of it ☐   Some of it ☐   None of it ☐
• **I am like** ☐ **unlike** ☐ **Georgia because** _____

_____ .

Activity 2 — Lost for Words

SB 96-97

▶ **Answer the questions.**

1. How does Georgia feel when she touches the stone.

   calm

2. What is wrong with the teacher?

   He is speaking strangely/saying a funny word.

3. What is wrong with Ms Vedden?

   She is using the funny word too.

4. What does Georgia's mother do?

   She also uses the funny word.

5. How does Georgia feel?

   shocked

6. What do you think *krowfosdrow* means?

   Answers will vary.

▶ **Check off the correct sentence on the stepping stone.**

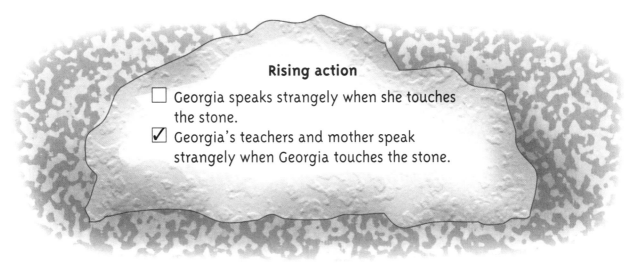

Rising action

☐ Georgia speaks strangely when she touches the stone.

☑ Georgia's teachers and mother speak strangely when Georgia touches the stone.

- **I think this part of the story is funny ☐ strange ☐ interesting ☐.**

Activity **3** Trouble for Georgia

SB 98-99

▶ **Answer the questions.**

1. How do the parents feel?

   suspicious; angry

2. How do the students feel?

   upset

3. What does Georgia realize?

   She has to stop touching the stone.

4. What does she want to do now?

   She wants to write everything down to tell her teacher.

▶ **Check off the correct sentences on the stepping stones.**

Climax
- ☑ Georgia decides to write everything down.
- ☐ Georgia decides to throw away the stone.

Rising action
- ☑ Georgia tests the rock.
- ☐ Georgia leaves the rock at home.

- ☐ The students are angry with Georgia.
- ☑ The students are upset because their grades are falling.

	Yes	No
• **My prediction was correct.**	☐	☐
• **I worked well with my partner.**	☐	☐

Well Done, Georgia!

> **Answer the questions.**

1. What does Mr Renzo say to Georgia?
   Well done, Georgia!

2. What does the word *krowfosdrow* mean?
   "words of work" spelled backwards

3. How did Georgia think of the story?
   She used her imagination.

> **Check off the correct sentence on the stepping stone.**

Resolution
- ☐ Georgia succeeds because she finds a lucky stone.
- ☑ Georgia succeeds because she uses her imagination.

Continued on next page

The Forgetting Stone

one hundred and nine

109

 **Well Done, Georgia! (continued)**

Readers' Rally

▶ **Find someone who can . . .**

The student who answers the question will sign the card.

1. Name one thing that Georgia likes. *chocolate ice cream; cats; rocks; magazines*	2. Name one thing that Georgia dislikes. *black jujubes; horses; thunderstorms*	3. Name one thing that Georgia hates. *school*	4. Repeat what Georgia wanted the teacher to say. *Well done, Georgia!*
5. Say what Georgia collects. *rocks/stones*	6. Describe the stone Georgia found. *colourful*	7. Say the funny word from the story. *krowfosdrow*	8. Say how the stone made Georgia feel. *calm*
9. Name the three people who forgot how to say certain words. *Mr Renzo; Ms Vedden; her mother*	10. Say which type of words disappeared. *words of work*	11. Say how the other students felt. *upset*	12. Say what the funny word means. *words of work*
13. Say what the climax of the story is. *Georgia writes everything down.*	14. Say how the story ends. *Georgia's teacher says, "Well done" and Georgia feels proud.*	15. Say where Georgia finds her ideas. *in her imagination*	16. Explain the title of the story. *The stone makes people forget words of work.*

- **I spoke English during the Readers' Rally.**
  Always ☐   Most of the time ☐   Some of the time ☐   Never ☐
- **I liked ☐ didn't like ☐ this story because** _____
  _____.

Story Map

► Complete the stepping stones
for Georgia's story.

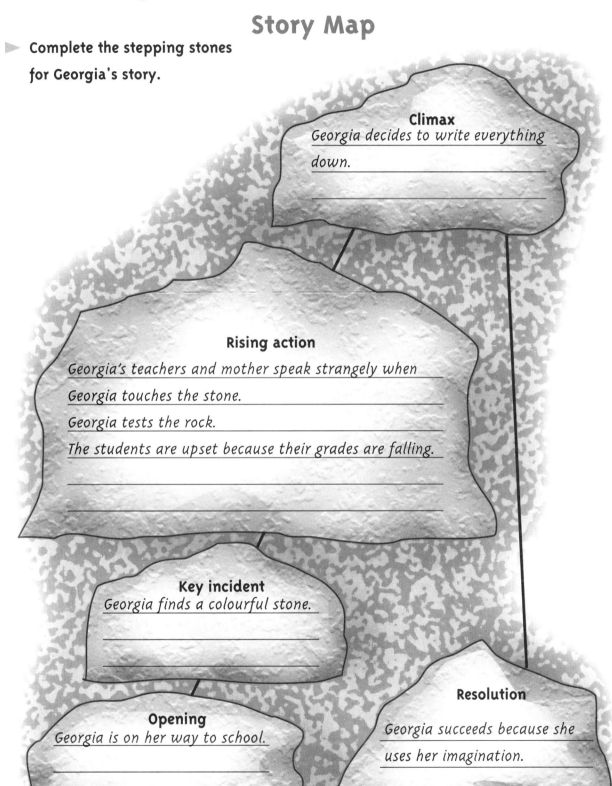

Climax
Georgia decides to write everything
down. _____
_____

Rising action
Georgia's teachers and mother speak strangely when
Georgia touches the stone.
Georgia tests the rock.
The students are upset because their grades are falling.
_____
_____

Key incident
Georgia finds a colourful stone.
_____
_____

Opening
Georgia is on her way to school.
_____
_____

Resolution
Georgia succeeds because she
uses her imagination.
_____

Continued on next page

The Forgetting Stone

My Story

▶ **Complete the stepping stones for your story.**

Students will complete the stepping stones for their own stories.

Climax
_____
_____
_____

Rising action
_____
_____
_____
_____
_____

Key incident
_____
_____

Resolution
_____
_____
_____

Opening
_____
_____

- **I made a story map for my own story.**   Yes ☐   No ☐
- **During this unit, I worked:**
  Very hard ☐   Moderately hard ☐   Not very hard ☐   Not hard at all ☐

Extension Activity

A Story of My Own

► **Use your story map to write and illustrate your own story.**

Students will write and illustrate their own stories.

And the Winner Is . . .

▶ Survey your classmates to discover which type of story is the most popular.

Name	Science Fiction	Biography	Mystery	Adventure	Fantasy	Horror
Students will conduct a survey to discover the most popular type of story.						
Totals						

The most popular type of story is _____ .

Unit 12

Rémi
Abdul | Thomas
Georgia | Karl
André | Karim | Doris
Sue-Ming | Marie | Gilles
Amanda | Barouk | Émilie
Miranda | Greta | Lori | Daniel
2001 | 2002 | 2003 | 2004 | 2005 | 200

The Welcome Wall

SB
104

▶ Write the unit numbers and titles.

▶ Match each statement with its unit.

	Unit __1__. *Learning Tools*	I discovered the meaning of friendship. *Unit 9*
	Unit __2__. *On This Day*	I compared toys from the present and the past. *Unit 4*
	Unit __3__. *Words of Honour*	I learned about some acts of courage. *Unit 6*
	Unit __4__. *Playing Around*	I reviewed what I studied in this book. *Unit 12*
	Unit __5__. *Fear Files*	I discovered what some names mean. *Unit 3*
	Unit __6__. *It Takes Courage*	I discovered what some people are afraid of. *Unit 5*
	Unit __7__. *Beat the Record*	I participated in a record-breaking event. *Unit 7*
	Unit __8__. *Celebrating the World*	I discovered some tools I can use when learning English. *Unit 1*
	Unit __9__. *Forever Friends*	I found out about my special day. *Unit 2*
	Unit __10__. *Signs of the Times*	I learned about some special celebrations around the world. *Unit 8*
	Unit __11__. *The Forgetting Stone*	I learned that imagination is a powerful tool. *Unit 11*
	Unit __12__. *The Welcome Wall*	I learned about the past, the present and the future. *Unit 10*

▶ **Fill in the form as you find the matching titles and activities.**

Unit	Wrap-up Activity
	Make a Learning Tools poster.
	Commemorate your special day.
	Design your personal coat of arms.
	Advertise your new toy.
	Create a Cave of Fears.
	Create a Heroes' Hall of Fame.

Continued on next page

 **Chatterbox Challenge (continued)**

Unit	Wrap-up Activity
	Make a Class Record Book.
	Prepare a scrapbook about a festival or celebration.
	Perform the play The Homecoming.
	Make a sign for your times.
	Make your own story map.
	Build a Welcome Wall.

Activity 2 — The Reader's Review

▶ Write the number of the summary beside the title of the story.

1. Take this advice: Don't look back!

2. In this story, the peasant is the noble one.

3. Imagination is a powerful tool.

4. A young girl learns the meaning of friendship.

Forever Friends ___4___

Down Under ___1___

The Keeper ___2___

The Forgetting Stone ___3___

Extension Activity

Our Story Markers

▶ Use one of the models to create a special way to remember your favourite Chatterbox story.

▶ Trace or photocopy the model and decorate your choice.

Students will create markers for their favourite Chatterbox stories.

Continued on next page

Enter into my favourite story.

Activity 3 Tools for Tomorrow

► **Use this page to list all the strategies you and your partner mention.**

Me	My partner
Answers will vary.	

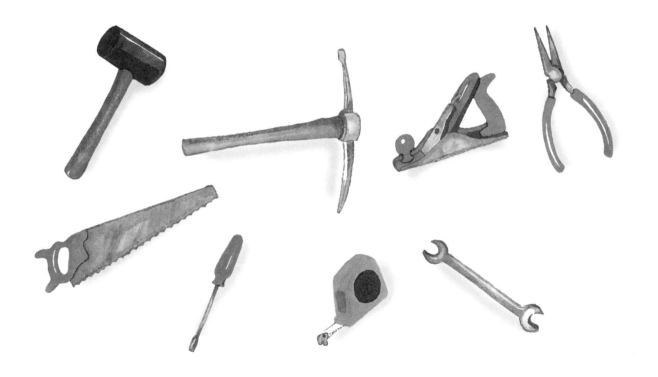

Activity 4 Super Cool!

▶ **Place each unit in one of the categories.**

	Super cool!	Cool!	Boring!
Answers will vary.			

Unit 1. Learning Tools

Unit 2. On This Day

Unit 3. Words of Honour

Unit 4. Playing Around

Unit 5. Fear Files

Unit 6. It Takes Courage

Unit 7. Beat the Record

Unit 8. Celebrating the World

Unit 9. Forever Friends

Unit 10. Signs of the Times

Unit 11. The Forgetting Stone

▶ **Complete the brick as you work through the unit.**

My favourite unit is: _____

My favourite wrap-up activity is: _____

My favourite story is: _____

My advice is: _____

Students will indicate their preferences as they work through the unit.

Word Quiz

▶ Find out how many words you have learned.

▶ Put a check next to each word you know and a ? next to those you are not certain of.

▶ Do this as quickly as you can.

Answers will vary.

sportswear ☐ ugly ☐ clay ☐

crowbar ☐ darkness ☐ dock ☐

cast ☐ audience ☐ pretend ☐

forever ☐ greet ☐ device ☐

candy cane ☐ proud ☐ blink ☐

butterfly ☐ bathe ☐ reach ☐

freedom ☐ level ☐ wallpaper ☐

available ☐ cheer ☐ lyrics ☐

lines ☐ key incident ☐ movable ☐

award ☐ closet ☐ challenge ☐

homecoming ☐ laugh at ☐ blindfolded ☐

Continued on next page

play ☐

harmful ☐

evil ☐

opening ☐

allow ☐

curtain ☐

embarrassed ☐

electric sander ☐

hammer ☐

diary ☐

carpenter's square ☐

heartbroken ☐

hop ☐

garbage ☐

phone booth ☐

ghost ☐

mallet ☐

flag ☐

electric drill ☐

full-length ☐

beat ☐

lonely ☐

electric saw ☐

pickaxe ☐

crowded ☐

fierce ☐

cardboard ☐

axe ☐

ferocious ☐

headlight ☐

performance ☐

kid ☐

push button ☐

lawn mower ☐

elevator ☐

Continued on next page

Word Quiz (continued)

washable ☐   whisper ☐   tough ☐

skunk ☐   hate ☐   thunderstorm ☐

tear ☐   resolution ☐   shelter ☐

hit ☐   smash ☐   sibling ☐

home ☐   track ☐   stuffed ☐

tape measure ☐   jump ☐   trick ☐

saw ☐   rocking chair ☐   rough ☐   upset ☐

hover ☐   screwdriver ☐   helmet ☐   ye ☐

shiver ☐   lean ☐   scrapbook ☐

please ☐   lovable ☐   wedding ☐

climax ☐   scream ☐   strength ☐

Continued on next page

treat ☐   lullaby ☐   heavy-duty ☐

struggle ☐   unbreakable ☐   perspire ☐

rotary dial ☐   scared ☐   stage ☐

script ☐   pit ☐   shake ☐

sweat ☐   smooth ☐   wisdom ☐

removable ☐   whistle ☐   reckless ☐

wrench ☐   snake ☐   pliers ☐

wolf ☐   plane ☐   shield ☐

rising action ☐   plot ☐   wonder ☐

prop ☐   tiny ☐   timeless ☐

sleigh ☐   shore ☐   steady ☐

Memory Wall

► Ask your friends and teachers to write farewell messages to you.